Stegosaurus:
ARMORED DEFENDER

by Kathryn Clay   illustrated by Jason Dove

CONSULTANT:
MATHEW J. WEDEL, PhD
PALEONTOLOGIST AND ASSISTANT PROFESSOR
WESTERN UNIVERSITY OF HEALTH SCIENCES, POMONA, CALIFORNIA

CAPSTONE PRESS
a capstone imprint

First Graphics are published by Capstone Press,
1710 Roe Crest Drive, North Mankato, Minnesota 56003.
www.capstonepub.com

Books published by Capstone Press are manufactured with paper
containing at least 10 percent post-consumer waste.

Library of Congress Cataloging-in-Publication Data
  Stegosaurus : armored defender / by Kathryn Clay.
     p. cm. — (First graphics. Dinosaurs)
  Includes bibliographical references and index.
  Summary: "In graphic novel format, text and illustrations present Stegosaurus, its
characteristics and probable behavior, and information about extinction"—Provided
by publisher.
  ISBN 978-1-4296-7604-5 (library binding)
  ISBN 978-1-4296-7929-9 (paperback)
  1. Stegosaurus—Juvenile literature. I. Title. II. Dove, Jason.

QE862.O65C53 2012
567.915'3—dc23   2011036562

EDITOR: LORI SHORES
DESIGNER: LORI BYE
ART DIRECTOR: NATHAN GASSMAN
PRODUCTION SPECIALIST: KATHY MCCOLLEY

Printed in the United States of America in Stevens Point, Wisconsin.
102011   006404WZS12

TABLE OF CONTENTS

MEET STEGOSAURUS

Something large moves through the trees. Bony plates stick up above the ferns.

STOMP! STOMP! STOMP!

Stegosaurus is in trouble. A hungry allosaurus is close behind.

AGE OF THE DINOSAURS

	298 mya		250 mya		208 mya	
		Permian Period		Triassic Period		Jurassic Period
	PALEOZOIC ERA			MESOZOIC ERA		

Allosaurus attacks. It avoids the stiff plates on stegosaurus' back.

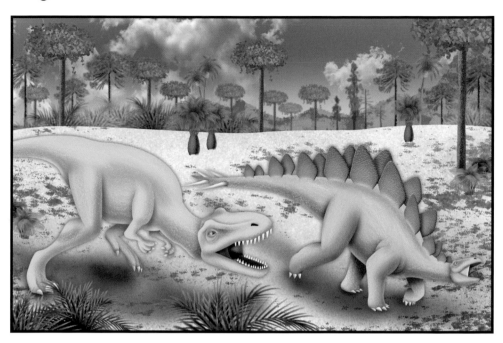

Stegosaurus swings its spiky tail.
This time, stegosaurus wins.

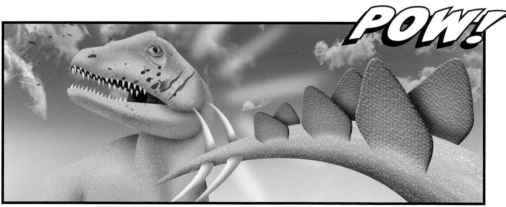

145 mya	65 mya	mya= millions of years ago
Cretaceous Period		
	CENOZOIC ERA	

Stegosaurus lived 150 million years ago. Much of the Earth was covered in trees and plants. The weather was warm and wet.

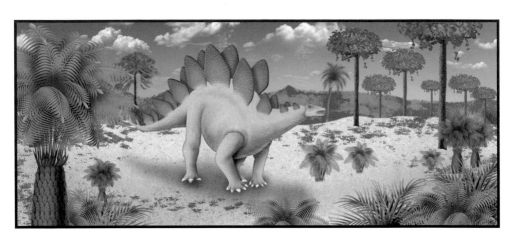

Stegosaurus lived in North America and Europe. Fossils have been found in the American west and in Portugal.

Where Stegosaurus lived

Stegosaurus was not alone. Many dinosaurs lived during this time.

Many dinosaurs ate meat. But not stegosaurus.

Stegosaurus only ate plants. Small herds traveled to find food.

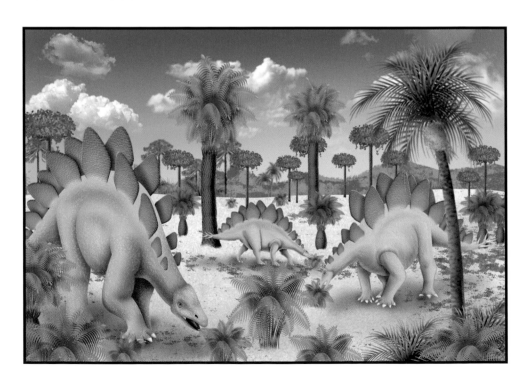

Its bony beak easily tore through plants. Stegosaurus chewed with tiny cheek teeth.

Stegosaurus swallowed small rocks. The rocks mashed up plants in the dinosaur's stomach.

BIG BODY, SMALL BRAIN

Stegosaurus weighed 2 to 3 tons (1.8 to 2.7 metric tons).

The dinosaur stood 12 feet (3.7 meters) tall and 25 feet (7.6 m) long. That's about the size of a school bus.

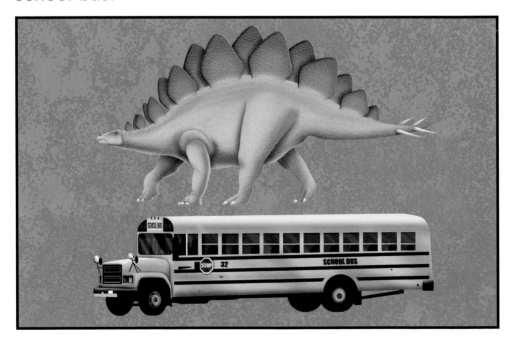

Stegosaurus moved slowly on short, fat legs. Its front claws tore up the ground.

Its head was small for such a big body. Stegosaurus' brain was only as big as a walnut.

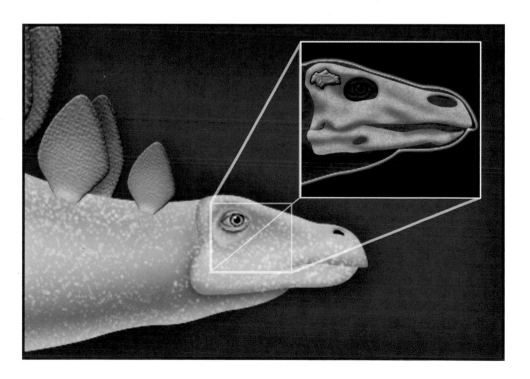

Seventeen hard plates stuck up from stegosaurus' neck and back.

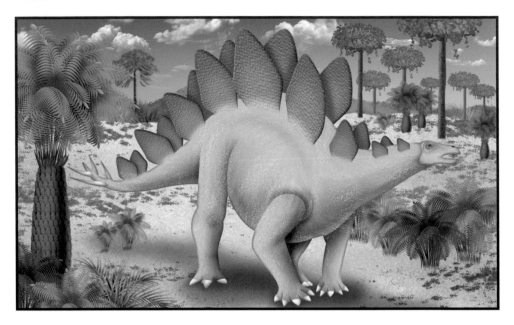

The plates were made of bone. A layer of hard keratin covered the plates.

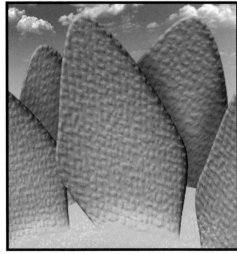

The largest plates were 3 feet (1 m) tall.

The plates helped stegosauruses tell each other apart from similar looking dinosaurs.

The plates may have also made stegosaurus look bigger to enemies.

DINO YOUNG

Like all dinosaurs, stegosaurus laid eggs.

Stegosaurus used its front claws to dig a nest in the ground.

Each nest held six or more eggs.

Adult stegosauruses may have guarded their nests
until the babies hatched.

DANGER!

Hungry meat-eaters were always looking for a meal. But stegosaurus had many defenses.

Tough scales made stegosaurus' skin hard to bite through.

The scales over stegosaurus' neck had bone inside
to make them extra strong.

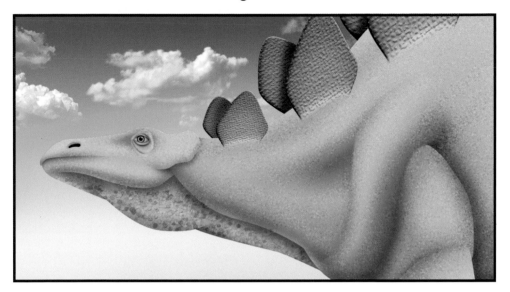

Stegosaurus' scales and plates were like
strong armor.

If an enemy did attack, stegosaurus had another defense.

Four sharp spikes made stegosaurus' tail a deadly weapon.

Stegosaurus swung its large tail from side to side.

The 2-foot (0.6 m) spikes easily cut through an enemy's skin.

Today you can only find stegosauruses in museums.

Stegosaurus died out about 135 million years ago.
Other dinosaurs lived for another 70 million years.

Over time, mud and sand covered stegosaurus' bones. The bones hardened into rocks called fossils.

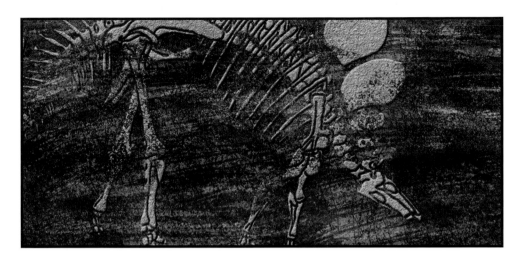

Scientists study fossils to learn more about this armored dinosaur.

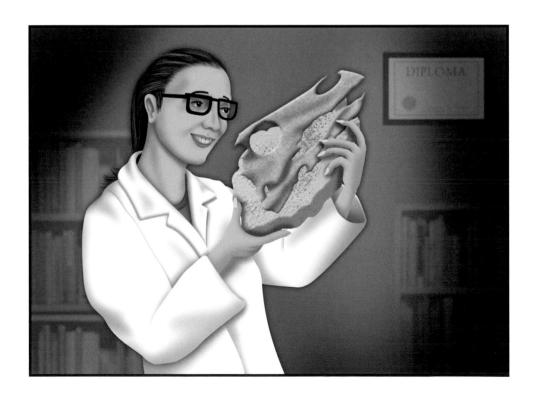

GLOSSARY

armor—bones, scales, and skin that some animals have on their bodies for protection

defense—a way to protect someone or something from an attack

fossil—remains of an ancient plant or animal that have hardened into rock

hatch—to break out of an egg

herd—a group of animals that live or move together

keratin—the hard substance that forms hair and fingernails

plate—a flat, bony growth

scale—one of the small pieces of hard skin covering the body of a fish, snake, or other reptile

READ MORE

Dodson, Peter. *Stegosaurus Up Close: Plated Dinosaur.* Zoom In on Dinosaurs! Berkeley Heights, N.J.: Enslow Publishers, 2011.

Olien, Rebecca. *How Do We Know About Dinosaurs? A Fossil Mystery.* Science Mysteries. Mankato, Minn.: Capstone Press, 2012.

Rockwood, Leigh. *Stegosaurus.* Dinosaurs Ruled! New York: PowerKids Press, 2012.

INTERNET SITES

FactHound offers a safe, fun way to find Internet sites related to this book. All of the sites on FactHound have been researched by our staff.

Here's all you do:

Visit *www.facthound.com*

Type in this code: 9781429676045

Check out projects, games and lots more at
www.capstonekids.com

INDEX

TITLES IN THIS SET: